You're Special

Lyrics by Mark Collier
Illustrated by Cesar E. De Castro
Painted by Papo de Asis'
Designed by Barry K. Haun

© 2001 Little Star Entertainment
   West Covina, California 91791

Published by the Character Building Company
West Covina, California 91791
www.characterbuilding.com
Printed in Korea
ISBN 1-931454-04-3

Library of Congress cataloging-in-publication data is available from the publisher.

Songs in this book are from the **Character Classics** series and are available on cassette and CD.
Coming soon the video series.

You're Special

Impromptu in A Flat Major, Op.90 No. 4 - Franz Schubert

I may have a large nose,
And yours may be small,
Or maybe you're shorter,
And I'm extra tall,
Your hair may be curly,
And mine may be straight,
You may not have freckles,
But I have ninety-eight.

You may have a low voice,
And mine may be high,
You may be outgoing,
And I may be shy,
We're all very different,
Like each shining star,
So learn to be happy,
Content with who you are.

You're special, I'm special,
The way that we are,
Believe that you're special,
And you will go far,
Be glad, happy, not sad,
Because you're special, I'm special.

You may be an athlete,
And I may like art,
You put things together,
I take them apart,
We're all very different,
Like each shining star,
So learn to be happy,
Content with who you are.

You're special, I'm special,
The way that we are,
Believe that you're special,
And you will go far,
Be glad, happy, not sad,
Because you're special, I'm special.

We're all very different,
Like each shining star,
So learn to be happy,
Content with who you are.
We're all very different,
Like each shining star,
So learn to be happy,
Content with who you are.

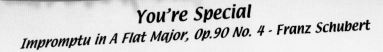

Now *picture* this song as you read or sing along...

And yours
may be small,

Or maybe you're
SHORTER

Your hair may be **CURLY**,

And mine may be STRAIGHT,

You may not have freckles,

But I have ninety-eight.

You may have a low voice,

You may be outgoing,

And I may be shy,

We're all very different,
Like each shining star,

So learn to be happy,
Content with who you are.

You're special, I'm special,
The way that we are,

Believe that you're special,
And you will go far,

Be glad, happy, not sad,
Because you're special, I'm special.

You may be an athlete,

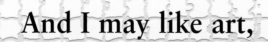

And I may like art,

You put things together,

I take them apart,

We're all very different,
Like each shining star,

So learn to be happy,
Content with who you are.

Believe that you're special,
And you will go far,

Be glad, happy, not sad,
Because you're special, I'm special.

We're all very different, like each shining star,
So learn to be happy, content with who you are.
We're all very different, like each shining star,
So learn to be happy, content with who you are.

Content With What You've Got

Eine Kleine Nachtmusik
Wolfgang Amadeus Mozart

Be content, content with what you've got,
Don't forget you've really got a lot!

Jenny went shopping at the store,
Had two, she wanted four,
She's grabbing more and more,
Just look at Jenny, Jenny has so many,
Others don't have any, Jenny has so much!

Jenny look around, settle down,
Stop that frown, it doesn't look good on you,
You'll feel good inside, satisfied, full of pride,
When you learn to…

Be content, content with what you've got,
Don't forget you've really got a lot!

Billy, he thought he had it rough,
His room was full of stuff,
But that was not enough,
Just look at Billy, isn't Billy silly,
Really, Billy, really,
Billy has so much!

Billy, look around, settle down,
Stop that frown, it doesn't look good on you,
You'll feel good inside, satisfied, full of pride,
When you learn to…

Be content, content with what you've got,
Don't forget you've really got a lot!
Be content, content with what you've got,
Don't forget you've really got a lot!

Sherri, she doesn't have a lot,
To her it matters not,
She's glad for what she's got,
Just look at Sherri, Sherri is so very,
Extraordinary, Sherri understands!

Take a look around, settle down,
Stop that frown, it doesn't look good on you,
You'll feel good inside, satisfied, full of pride,
When you learn to…

Be content, content with what you've got,
Don't forget you've really got a lot!
Be content, content with what you've got,
Don't forget you've really got a lot!

You've got to be content,
You've got to be content with what you've got!

Little Theodore

The Seasons - November
Peter Tchaikovsky

Little Theodore, always wanting more,
Never satisfied, he is such a chore,
No one's ever seen him content before,
Always wanting more, little Theodore.

I am Theodore, and I want some more,
I'm not satisfied, is it such a chore?
No one's ever seen me content before,
I want more and more
Just for me, little Theodore.

At the store little Theodore, something caught his eye,
Now he's squirming, pleading, always needing,
Something new, not just one or two,
He wants three or four,
Theodore's grabbing, everything nabbing,
Poking and jabbing 'til he gets it!

Little Theodore, always wanting more,
Never satisfied, he is such a chore,
No one's ever seen him content before,
Always wanting more, little Theodore.

I am Theodore, and I want some more,
I'm not satisfied, is it such a chore?
No one's ever seen me content before,
I want more and more
Just for me, little Theodore.

Theodore at the ocean shore,
When it's time to go,
Theodore starts delaying, always saying,
"One more time, give me one last swim,
Let me go back in,"
Then he starts yelling, whining, and wailing,
Running and flailing 'till he gets to!

Little Theodore, always wanting more,
Never satisfied, he is such a chore,
No one's ever seen him content before,
Always wanting more, little Theodore.

And we won't be like little Theodore
Never satisfied, always wanting more.
Learn to be content, it's not such a chore,
Let's be satisfied, not like Theodore!
He wants more and more, little Theodore!

Edgar the Elephant

Le Carnaval des Animaux-L'Elephant
Camille Saint-Saëns

My name is Edgar, I never thought much of me,
I'm big and lumpy, kinda clumsy.
Very slow, can't even climb a tree,
Big ears, four big feet, I've got a long windy nose,
I break all the toys and make lots of noise,
Wherever I goes.

Now instead of what I can't do, don't wanna be,
Concentrate on what I can do, who I can be,
I'm not the way I oughta be,
I'm gonna be content with me, now I see…

I'm big, but I'm strong, and I have incredible size,
To push and pull things, lift and drag things,
Don't forget I'm very, very wise,
When I go swimming, I always make a big splash,
I spray like a hose and out of my nose,
A trumpet can blast!

Now instead of what I can't do, don't wanna be,
Concentrate on what I can do, who I can be,
I'm not the way I oughta be,
I'm gonna be content with me, now I see…

So listen to Edgar the elephant and you'll see,
It's not the can'ts and not the don'ts
But what we can do, who we all can be,
Thank you, dear Edgar, for showing us,
That we all have special qualities,
And now I'll learn to be content with me!

My Memory Box

The Reaper's Song
Robert Schumann

I have a box that is filled with good memories,
I take it with me wherever I go,
Open it up and there's so much contentment,
These are the favorite memories I know.

The smell of fresh popcorn, a clown at the circus,
Some pink cotton candy, a hot dog and fries,
A ride on my bike through a giant mud puddle,
And friends at my house for my birthday surprise.

I have a box that is filled with good memories,
Memories that take all my sadness away,
Open it up and there's so much contentment,
I fill it up with good memories each day.

A trip to the ocean, a perfect sand castle,
The wind in my hair and the sun on my face,
A triple scoop sundae that's smothered in chocolate,
The day Dad and I won a three-legged race.

I have a box that is filled with good memories,
I take it with me wherever I go,
Open it up and there's so much contentment,
These are the favorite memories I know.

Of camping and fishing on summer vacation,
The night before Christmas, I hardly can wait,
A cold winter night warming up by the fire,
A cup of hot chocolate and staying up late!

I have a box that is filled with good memories,
Memories that take all my sadness away,
Open it up and there's so much contentment,

I fill it up with good memories each day.
I fill it up with good memories each day.
Filling it up with good memories each day.

Fine.

fee´·nay
A musical term for the end.